LIBRARY

CANTERBURY CHRIST CHURCH COLLEGE

D0808246

as a holiday

Adapted by: Pamela Egan
Pictures: Dea de Vries

fice
Yard, London SW1P 3NZ

Hello, Lisa!
We can see you!
Lisa is on holiday.
At home she lives in a flat.
The flat is in a big town.
But on holiday she lives in this tent.
Lucky Lisa!
This is her first time in a tent.

When you live in a tent
you can have dinner outside.
Lisa and her brother Rob
and her Mum and Dad all do that.
Lisa can see lots of birds.
They even hop on to the table
to get the crumbs.
Lisa likes that.

Lisa plays with Gary and Tessa.
They live in the next tent.
They are on holiday too.
A tent is a bit small to play in.
Dad says, 'Come on –
you can have a tent of your own.'
Dad and Lisa pick up sticks.

Lisa and Gary make a tent.
They make it out of sticks and a blanket.
They need a lot of sticks!
It is a bit hot under the blanket
but they like it.

Dad has a bike.
Lisa sits on the back of the bike.
Gary and Tessa see them go.
They are going to meet Mum
and Rob.
They ride down the road.

A cow looks at them over a fence.
She has big brown eyes.
'What do we get from a cow?' asks Dad.
'What?' says Lisa.
'Milk,' says Dad.
'But milk comes out of bottles,' says Lisa.
Dad grins. 'It comes out of a cow first!' he says.

Mum and Rob are here.
'Let's go into the woods,' says Mum.
They all go into the shade of the trees.
The woods smell fresh and damp.
The grass is soft.
They find a pool of clear water.
Lisa likes it.

Ssh… can you hear?
All the birds are singing.

Lisa's flip-flops go flip, flop on the grass.
The grass is soft between her toes.
Look, here's a table!
'We can have a picnic,' says Dad.

'I have some buns in my bag,' says Mum.
She looks.

'Oh, Mum!' says everybody.
'You forgot them!'
'Sorry, birds,' says Lisa.
'No crumbs.'
'Never mind,' says Dad.
'I have a plan.'

Rob says, 'And I have some crisps.'
They eat the crisps.
Birds like crisps, too.
Lisa gives some to the birds.
'Come on,' says Dad.
'It's time for my plan.'

They go back to the road.
Down the road is a café
'My plan is fish and chips
    for everybody,' says Dad.
Lisa has room for pancakes too.
She likes that!

Next day they all play
a good game.
Dad goes into the wood.
He takes some red string.
He puts some red string on the trees.
Then he hides.
Lisa and Rob and Gary and Tessa
    have to follow him.
The string shows them where to go.
It takes them a long time to find Dad.
Lisa likes that game.

Next day Lisa finds some flowers.
They look so pretty.
Lisa picks a bunch of flowers.
She holds them in her warm hand.
But the flowers die.
Mum says, 'Don't pick the flowers.
Let them grow.
Then everybody can see them.'
So next time Lisa just looks
at the flowers.

It's time for bed.
The sky is dark blue.
Lisa looks out of the tent window.
She can see lots of stars in the sky.
It is all so still.
She can hear the leaves on the trees.
They go 'Wssssh…' in the wind.
Lisa likes that.
She likes her holiday in a tent.
Sleep well, Lisa!

Notes for parents and teachers:

This Benjamin Book is one of a series which deals with children's important experiences — going to school for the first time, having a country holiday, moving house, going to hospital, getting a new baby in the family, having a birthday. (It may be helpful to know that *Joe has a new house* is about a one-parent family.)

They can be used just as a basis for shared talk and discussion about these experiences, some of which can be disturbing for young children. These stories allow them a chance to question and give adults the opportunity to help and reassure them. But the stories can also be used, if you so wish, as part of religious teaching. The wonders of God's world, people who help us, the joys of friendship and sharing are implicit in the stories and can be linked to religious teaching or lead into prayers related to the children's own needs.

Produced by arrangement with Nederlandsche Zondagsschool Vereeniging Amsterdam.

© English Text: Central Board of Finance of the Church of England, 1978.